CHRISTMAS
Program Builder
No. 36

Graded Plays—Pantomimes—Recitations
—Songs—Exercises

Compiled by Paul M. Miller

Permission to make photocopies of program
builders is granted to the purchaser when three
books have been purchased. The photocopies cannot be sold, loaned, or given away.

Lillenas Publishing Co.
KANSAS CITY, MO. 64141

A Guarantee

It always works;
 It's always true—
Christmas love
 Comes back to you.

—Debra Dumas

Happy Singing

Sing, oh, sing a happy song.
Love the Saviour all day long.
He who came to earth one day,
Slept in a manger filled with hay.

—Debra Dumas

Long Ago

(For three wee children)

FIRST CHILD—
In a manger full of hay
Slept a babe on Christmas Day.

SECOND CHILD—
All the world was fast asleep,
Except some shepherds and their
 sheep.

THIRD CHILD—
An angel in the dark, black sky;
Told of Jesus, who did not cry.

ALL—
Then He was a little boy;
And now He is our Christmas Joy.

—Debra Dumas

Christmas Manger

(Table stands in front of audience. Five children enter and stand behind table. Each steps in front to speak and to place figure in the manger scene.)

FIRST CHILD *(with stable)—*
Little Baby Jesus
 Was born in a stable.
His mama told Him to be brave,
 As much as He was able.

SECOND CHILD *(with Mary)—*
Gentle Mother Mary
 Loved Him very much.
She wrapped Him in a blanket warm,
 To keep from winter's touch.

THIRD CHILD *(with Joseph)—*
Joseph guarded Jesus
 And watched Him sleep on hay.
He knew that God the Father
 Loved Him night and day.

FOURTH CHILD *(with shepherd)—*
Shepherds on a hillside
 Heard the angels' song.
They came to Baby Jesus
 And worshipped all night long.

FIFTH CHILD *(with lamb)—*
Maybe shepherds brought Him
 A lamb with wool so white.
If I could give Him anything,
 I'd give my heart and life.

—Anna Medford

2

Christmas Bells

Bells are chiming o'er the earth
Bringing news of Jesus' birth.

—*Lois Sink*

Just a Little Child

Though I am just a little child,
I have some things to say.
Because another little child
Was born on Christmas Day.

—*Elanor Frances Giel*

Welcome

(Child enters and bows.)

Of all the days,
In all the year;
I think Christmas is
The one most dear.

—*Anna Medford*

Peace and Love

A message of peace
For men on earth.
A message of love,
A holy birth.

—*Elanor Frances Giel*

My Big Gift

(Child enters carrying large box. On cue he removes top and takes out a heart cut from paper or a pillow.)

If I could put this
Under your tree,
I'd put on a card

That says, "Just from me."
Inside it you'd find
Something so true;
(removes heart)
Just a reminder
That God really loves you.

—*Tim Allen*

Christmas Morn

In the quiet and the stillness
Of that early Christmas morn,
Christ, the Savior, came from heaven,
In a stable to be born.

—*Lois Sink*

Christmas Secrets

Mother's baking cookies;
Sister's at the store;
Daddy's at his workbench;
We have secrets galore!

But this is no secret . . .
Have a Happy Christmas!

—*A. F. Dumas*

Another Welcome

I'm not very tall
And not very fat.
Nothing's got my tongue,
Not even the cat.

So I can declare,
With all of my might,
We're glad you're all here
For our program tonight!

—*Anna Medford*

Message of the Bells

(Three children enter with a bell or string of sleigh bells.)

FIRST CHILD—
Ring the bells on Christmas Day;
Ring the bells and let them say,

SECOND CHILD—
Christ is born to live and grow,
That we might learn to love Him so;

THIRD CHILD—
To live a life of peace and cheer,
To love each other all the year.

—*Elanor Frances Giel*

My Heart Belongs to Jesus

My heart belongs to Jesus;
  Because He loves me so,
He came to earth from heaven above
  So many years ago.

—Lois Sink

Shepherd Joy

The shepherds with their flocks at
    night
Awakened by a holy light.
Good news of joy was brought to
    them:
"Peace on earth, good will to men."

—Elanor Frances Giel

Welcome

Welcome to our program;
  To hear us speak and sing
About the Baby Jesus,
  The little newborn King.

—Lois Sink

Manger Song

Born in a manger,
A servant of men,
Born in a manger
In Bethlehem.

As He grew,
This special Son,
Mary knew
He was the One.

—Maria Nasick

Shepherds' Worship

The shepherds on the hillside
  Heard the angel's tidings ring,
And came with haste to worship Him,
  The newborn King of kings.

—Lois Sink

Worshiping Jesus

Oh, we can come to Jesus
  With our gifts of love today.
And then go forth to serve Him,
  His holy will obey.

—Lois Sink

What Christmas Means

1ST CHILD— Christmas means presents and giving of toys,
         Wrappings and tinsel and things that give joy.

2ND CHILD—Lights shining out on the snow-covered nights,
         Stars gleaming down from the heavens so bright.

3RD CHILD—Shopping and laughing, surprises galore,
         But Christmas to me means so much more.

4TH CHILD—It means sheep and shepherds on hillside forlorn.
         Angels proclaiming the Christ Child was born.

5TH CHILD—Mary and Joseph, the Babe on the hay—
         This is the meaning of glad Christmas Day.

—Lois Sink

Christmas

An Acrostic for Nine Children

(Each child carries a letter for his line, and on the back of the cards will be printed JOY JOY JOY.)

C (J) Christ came to earth on Christmas Day;

H (O) His bed was in the manger hay.

R (Y) Ringing out upon the air,

I (J) Into town and country there,

S (O) Singing happy songs of love,

T (Y) The angels praised His name above.

M (J) Many shepherds worshipped Him,

A (O) And wise men brought their gifts to Him.

S (Y) Salvation came through Christ our King.

ALL: With happy hearts we join to sing.

(The piano strikes the first chord for "Joy to the World," three times. On the first chord, the first three children turn their cards to read JOY, and to sing the word. On the second chord, the next three children turn their cards and sing, then the third group. All nine children then join to sing one stanza only of "Joy to the World.")

—*Elanor Pankow*

Twinkle, Twinkle

(Child holds a large, glitter-covered star which is moved back and forth to twinkle during recitation.)

Twinkle, twinkle, special star;
Angels tell us what you are,
Pointing to the manger stall,
Where lay a baby new and small.
He was born a Savior, King,
And that is why we want to sing.

—*Eleanor Pankow*

Three Wise Men

(Three boys costumed as wise men; each carries a traditional gift.)

FIRST BOY—
We wise men
have traveled far,
To praise the King of Kings.

SECQND BOY—
Bearing gifts,
we came to find
A child in Bethlehem.

THIRD BOY—
A star we followed
from the East
To a manger bed.

ALL—
We found a child
sleeping there,
Just as the prophets said.

—*Elanor Frances Giel*

5

Christmas Reason

In this Christmas season
 We are gathered here
For a special reason—
 To spread some Christmas cheer.

—*Elanor Frances Giel*

J-O-Y

J—is for Jesus
 Who cares about you.
O—is for others—
 He cares for them, too.
Y—is for Yuletide—
 the Christmas season.

These letters together
 Spell the word *joy.*
It's Jesus' wish
 For each girl and boy!

—*Thelma A. Karg*

Peace Acrostic

(Each child holds a decorated letter.)

P—Please let us welcome you,

E—Each one.

A—And say we wish you

C—Christmas cheer, cheer to

E—Everyone.

O—On Christmas morning long ago,

N—Noel, the angels sang.

E—Even now with joy we sing

A—And ring the bells of peace.

R—Ready each one

T—The Lord to praise,

H—Hosanna, let us sing.

—*Elanor Frances Giel*

The Manger and the Cross

(Eleven children carrying letters perform this recitation.)

M is for the *manger* in which the Savior lay,

A is for the *angels* who sang upon that day.

N is for the keeper's *"NO!"* that kept them from the inn.

G is for Christ's *glorious* birth to save man from his sin.

E is for *everyone* for whom Christ came that way.

R is for *redemption* He offers us this day.

C is for the *Cross* on which our Savior died,

R is for *redemption* He offers from His side.

O is for the *offering* of Christ's blood upon the tree,

S is for our *sins,* from which He set us free.

S is also for our *Savior,* who lives eternally.

(IN UNISON)
From the manger to the Cross, we have a story, real and true,
A story of God's precious love, meant for me and you.
The gift of freedom and of love—
How can I refuse? I will accept the Savior's love.
Now, how about *you?*

—*C. R. Scheidies*

The Cost of Christmas

(A recitation for seven children. Each wears a costume or carries a symbol or picture to illustrate his stanza. All speak together on the final stanza.)

1ST CHILD *(with wrapped gifts)*—
"It costs so much at Christmas,"
   We often hear folks say,
"To buy the gifts and presents,
   The tree and trimmings gay."

2ND CHILD *(girl dressed as Mary)*—
But then I think of Mary,
   And of the price she paid;
As in a manger on some hay,
   Her newborn Child she laid.

3RD CHILD *(boy dressed as king)*—
And then there were the wise men
   Who braved the deserts wild
To bring their gifts of value rare,
   To Bethlehem's newborn Child.

4TH CHILD *(boy or girl dressed as angel, holding baby)*—
It cost the God of heaven
   His only begotten Son,
But He gave Him, oh, so freely,
   That lost men might be won.

5TH CHILD *(boy carrying a cross)*—
It cost the blessed Son of God
   The very life He breathed
When He hung on Calvary that we
   From sin might be made free.

6TH CHILD *(girl with purse)*—
Yes, Christmas is expensive,
   But money cannot buy
Peace and love and happiness,
   Nor a home in heaven on high.

7TH CHILD *(boy with cut-out heart)*—
Yet these are things that God has planned
   In love for you and me;
They do not cost us money—
   They're absolutely free.

ALL THE CHILDREN—
If we will only trust the Christ
   Who in the manger lay,
Who gave His life to ransom ours,
   To heaven made a way.
                                    —*Lois Sink*

Manger Story

In a manger far away
A babe was born on Christmas Day.
Wise men traveled from afar,
Led to Jesus by a star.

                          —*Elanor Frances Giel*

Bells Ring

Christmas bells ring today;
Christmas bells, they seem to say,
"Awake, O men of earth, and see
A child is born for you and me."

                          —*Elanor Frances Giel*

Why?

(A recitation for four children)

1. Why do you think the angels sang
   So sweetly on that night?

2. Why do you think the stars that
   shone
   Were twinkling extra bright?

3. Why do you think the shepherds
   hurried
   To Bethlehem afar?

4. Why do you think the wise men
   came,
   Following His star?

ALL: Because the news from God
   above
   Told of the gift of His great
   love,
   Of Baby Jesus, born to be
   The Savior King for you and
   me.

                          —*Eleanor Pankow*

7

Ages 9-11

Lesson from a Candle

(Six children enter carrying lighted candles.)

FIRST CHILD—

A lighted candle
    Burning bright,
God's only Son
    Now in our sight.

SECOND CHILD—

The candle's flame
    A sign of joy:
God's only Son
    A baby boy.

THIRD CHILD—

The candle's warmth
    A sign of peace:
God's loving care
    Will never cease.

FOURTH CHILD—

The burning candle
    Lights our road;
The Son of God
    Now bears our load.

FIFTH CHILD—

The burning candle
    Draws us near;
The love of God
    Calms all our fears.

SIXTH CHILD—

The candle's flame
    May burn so low,
But the light of Jesus
    Will ever glow.

—Maria Nasick

The Christmas Wreath

(Five boys and girls enter carrying a large evergreen wreath. Each shares his or her stanza of the poem. As a final act, the wreath is hung as part of the auditorium decorations.)

SPEAKER 1—

There's something about a Christmas wreath
    That spreads the Yuletide cheer;
Reminds us the grace of God,
    When faith and hope are near.

SPEAKER 2—

The evergreen, eternal life,
    To those who do believe;
The berries red, the Savior's blood,
    Forgiveness to receive.

SPEAKER 3—

The bow reflects attractive love,
    The beauty of God's plan;
Display the wreath to public view,
    To symbol grace to man.

SPEAKER 4—

A wreath is made by human skill,
    But God makes loving grace;
But both are shared at Christmastime
    With all the human race.

SPEAKER 5—

So put a wreath upon your door,
    And let its message teach.
Then share the Christmas story,
    That others will be reached.

—E. L. Russell

A Little Prayer

I listened and caught,
    As it passed through the air,
A message from God
    In a little prayer.

I'll tell it to you—
    Now listen with care
To the message God sent
    Which I want to share.

"Hear Me, dear child,
    I care about you,
Not only at Christmas,
    But all the year through!"
        —Thelma A. Karg

The Lights of Christmas

1ST CHILD *(dressed as Joseph, carrying a lantern)*—

The inn was darkened, but the barn
    Displayed a tiny light:
A rude oil lamp that clearly showed
    A baby's face that night.

2ND CHILD *(dressed as angel)*—

An angel's glory light shone round
    The fields of Bethlehem,
And shepherds heard a heavenly
       choir
    That brought good news to them.

3RD CHILD *(wise man, holding paper star)*—

A brilliant star shone down from
       heaven
    To guide those traveling
Along the wise men's long, long road
    To find the newborn King.

4TH CHILD *(modern dress, holding candle)*—

Tonight we use electric bulbs
    And lovely candles bright,
Reminding us of our Light, Christ,
    Who takes away sin's night.

        —Anna Marie Dahlquist

My Message

The special message which I bring,
The message which the angels sing,
Tells of hope this Christmas morn,
Tells of Baby Jesus born.
        —Elanor Frances Giel

Christmastime

Christmas is a time to give,
A time to love, a time to live.
All of this because God gave
His only Son the world to save.
        —Elanor Frances Giel

To Honor Thee

(Use before offering.)

Dear Lord, we come to honor Thee,
    As wise men did of yore;
In humble love we bow to Thee
    Whom all our hearts adore.

Dear Lord, to honor Thee, we bring
    Our gifts, and tho' they're small,
With them we give our loving hearts,
    Our faith, our lives, our all.
        —Dorothy Conant Stroud

Pretty Candles

Shine, pretty candles,
    Shine on Christmas Day.
Shine out with cheerful gladness
    To brighten someone's way.

Shine, pretty candles,
    Shine out far and wide.
Spread joy throughout the earth
    And may peace and love abide.

Shine, pretty candles,
    At this season of the year.
Perhaps your little light
    Might fill some heart with cheer.
        —Helen Kitchell Evans

When We Find Him

The shepherds came to Bethlehem,
  To see God's little Boy.
And they not only found Him,
  But also peace and joy.

We seek the loving Savior,
  To worship at His feet,
We find He gives forgiveness
  And makes our lives complete.

—E. L. Russell

Make My Heart a Cradle

Little Christ child, soundly sleeping,
  Baby lambs are standing near;
Angels watch in skies above You;
  Sleep, small Jesus, never fear!

Little Jesus, blessed Christ child,
  Make my heart a cradle for
All the love You came to bring me;
  Help me love You even more!

—Dorothy Conant Stroud

Jesus

(An exercise for five children. Each carries a different large teaching picture suggested by the stanza. Mounted on the picture is a letter from the name Jesus.)

J Jesus was just a tiny Child
    When the shepherds saw His star
  Above the inn at Bethlehem
    As it guided them from afar.

E Even great kings and wise men knelt
    Before the Child's rude manger bed,
  While Mary and Joseph hovered near,
    Shielding their Son from strife ahead.

S "Surely this Child is God's own Son,"
    The gathering throng had murmured low,
  Then gazed in wonder as someone said,
    "Look, round His head—a heavenly glow!"

U Underneath the star's bright light
    Within a stable warmed by love
  The holy Infant slept secure
    While angels watched Him from above.

S Sleep, precious Baby, sleep in peace;
    May visions in Your dreams be blest
  Though pain and turmoil is Your fate,
    For You are God's love made manifest!

—Gladys M. Seiders

10

A Gift for Mom and Dad

(A Short Play)

By Paul M. Miller

Characters:

VINCE—	A brother
TONY—	A brother
JAN—	Their sister
MOTHER—	A voice from another room
CAROLERS—	Sing offstage

Setting:

The scene is set in the brothers' unkempt bedroom. TONY sits on the edge of the unmade bed; sister JAN is next to him. VINCE is studying a catalog. He sits at a table. The setting may be improvised to fit any requirements.

VINCE *(studying catalog)*—Boy, look at this grandfather clock. Wouldn't Mom and Dad like that?

TONY—Get smart, Vince. Take a look at the price tag.

VINCE—Oh, yeah, twelve hundred and fifty-two . . .

JAN *(interrupting)*—I still think we ought to get individual gifts for Mother and Daddy.

VINCE—Nah, it'll look like more if we pool our money.

TONY—What money?

JAN—I have $5.00 left from helping Mrs. Smith clean house. How much do you have, Vince?

VINCE—That's for me to know.

TONY—I'll tell you how much he's got—zero! That's why he wants to pool our money.

11

MOTHER *(voice from another room)*—Do you kids have your rooms picked up yet?

JAN—I've done mine, Mother, but these boys are just fooling around.

(TONY *jumps up and threatens* JAN.)

TONY—With a sister like you, who needs a pet rattlesnake?

MOTHER *(still from other room)*—Just remember, you're not going shopping until you get your chores done. After all, I can't keep—

VINCE and TONY *(together)*—Yes, Mom.

JAN—Come on, you guys, let's make up our minds. What are we going to get Mother and Daddy for Christmas?

TONY—Let's get them something that we *all* can enjoy.

VINCE—How about the 10-speed in the hardware store window?

TONY—Or a trampoline. Boy, wouldn't Mom and Dad just love one of those? I can see Mom now. *(Does a few dainty bounces.)*

JAN—For the last time, are we going to pool our money, or each buy individual gifts? *(Boys shrug their shoulders.)* All right, then, I'm going to make a decision—we're pooling. How much do each of you have?

(The boys look sheepish.)

VINCE—Well, I got into my saivngs to pay some library fines, and—

JAN—And what?

VINCE—I guess I'd better come clean; I bought a new seat for my bike—one of those Italian racing kind.

JAN—But Dad said you were to save enough out of your allowance for—

TONY—Jan?

JAN *(unhappily)*—What is it, Tony?

TONY—I'm broke too.

JAN—Oh, good grief!

MOTHER *(voice from other room)*—Jan, have those boys started on their room yet?

JAN—Not quite, Mother.

MOTHER *(voice)*—They'd better get started.

VINCE—What're we gonna do?

JAN—I have an idea; listen to this. *(Starts to whisper.)* First, we'll . . .

(Curtain closes during JAN'S *line, or there is a blackout. During this time the following poem may be recited. The reader should hold a long, long gift list. He or she stands in front of the curtain, or spotlighted to one side of the stage.)*

My Christmas List

Tissue paper, ribbons, bows;
Shopping lists and aching toes.

Do we fancy this the way
To celebrate a Christmas Day?

Gifts for Mama, Grandad, Lee,
But empty purse for poor ole me.

Gimme this and gimme that.
(Hope this shirt fits cousin Nat.)

Shopping days are dwindling down;
Shops are packed all over town.

But in the rush and in the race,
Let us pause to see His face.

Let us stop and think a while,
'Bout the manger and the Child.

Christmas lists are fun and nice,
But at the top is Jesus Christ.

What to give Him? How to show
We are aware of what we owe?

Give our love and give our life,
That way Christmas has no strife.

Act 2

(When the curtain opens, we see that the bed is made and the room has been straightened. JAN is typing at the table, VINCE and TONY stand behind her and read over her shoulder.)

VINCE—Hurry, Jan. We gotta finish this so we can get to the store before it closes.

JAN *(hunting and pecking on typewriter)*—"And this we hereby promise. Your sons . . ." *(Pulls paper out of typewriter.)* Now it's ready for you guys to sign.

TONY—Here, let me read it first.

VINCE—Read it out loud. I want to know what I'm signing.

(JAN gives the paper to TONY, who scans it.)

TONY—Looks pretty good, even though you did the typing.

JAN—"Even though." Well, let's see you boys get along without my services to this family. Why, who took your turns vacuuming last Saturday? And who got this room looking good just a few minutes ago?

13

VINCE—Okay, okay, Jan, we're convinced. Go ahead and read, Tony.

TONY *(reading)*—"Merry Christmas to you, Mom and Dad. The house is really getting Christmasy feeling. Specially in the living room and mostly under the tree. We know that you two have some super surprises for us—you always do. The three of us sure do wish that we could give you gifts in the same way you give them to us. But we guess that won't be possible for a while longer." Here, Vince, you read some of it. (TONY *hands the paper to* VINCE.)

VINCE *(reading)*—"So here is what the three of us want to give you as a main gift—a pledge that says the following: 'On this 25th day of December, we, your children, Jan, Tony, and Vince'"—I think my name ought to be first!

JAN—What d'ya mean, your name first? Girls' names are always first.

TONY—Go ahead and read, Vince. We can talk about that later.

VINCE—Okay, where was I? Oh, yeah—"We, your children, Jan, Tony, and *Vince,* do hereby promise that we will do our chores without too much pressure from you; we will make our beds regularly; we will try to keep the spirit of Christmas all year long. This we promise to do with God's help. Lovingly, your children . . .'"

JAN—"Jan,"

TONY—"Tony,"

VINCE—and "Vince."

MOTHER *(voice from other room)*—Hurry, children, there are carolers coming down the street.

CAROLERS *(singing offstage)*—"Joy to the world, the Lord is come" etc.

JAN—Know what, dear brothers?

TONY AND VINCE—What?

JAN—This just could be a super Christmas.

VINCE—Yeah! Know what I think is in the big box with the gold ribbon? I think it's a—

JAN—Knock it off, brother. That's not what I'm talking about. Maybe we can convince Mother and Daddy that we know what Christmas is really all about.

TONY—I think we do. "The Lord is come."

(CAROLERS *continue to sing as the three exit. Then* VINCE *runs back into the room and retrieves the letter they had written. He exits. Curtain.)*

The Night He Came

(A short, two-act play for junior highers)

by Beulahmae W. Marchbanks

Characters

JEREMY *(the innkeeper; wears beard)*

LEAH *(innkeeper's wife)*

JOSEPH *(also bearded)*

MOTHER *(guest at the inn)*

MARDA, ESTHER, and RUTH *(daughters)*

(Dress all characters in typical robes, etc., usually associated with Bible times.)

Staging

Scene I: A very plain room, table, and two chairs

Scene II: The balcony above the main room in the inn. (People lie, side by side, on the floor, sleeping.)

Back wall of balcony has small, two-foot-square window opening.

Scene I

(JEREMY, the innkeeper, and his wife, LEAH, sit at the table, where they count the day's receipts by candlelight. There is a pile of coins of different sizes in center of table. JEREMY holds a money bag.)

JEREMY—Look, wife, at the money for this day's counting! Never have we had such a good crowd to spend the night at this humble inn. Every wee corner is filled up. We couldn't cram in another one.

15

LEAH—Yes, my husband, it's true. I dare say, not a mouse could find a corner this night.
(Knock on the door)

JEREMY—Another traveler to turn away, no doubt. *(Goes to door and opens it wide.)*

JOSEPH—Please, sir, could we find lodging for the night? My wife—

JEREMY—I'm sorry, there is no room left. We can't house another person. You'll have to go on. Perhaps—

JOSEPH—But, sir, my wife is expecting a child. She can go no further.

JEREMY—That's sad, indeed it is, but I cannot help you. Look for yourself. *(He steps aside and Joseph enters, looks around.)*

JOSEPH—The stable, then? Have you a corner with hay? We could spread a bed there.

JEREMY—The stable? Why didn't I think of that sooner? I've turned away a dozen others. Oh, well, come. I'll show you. It's this way.

LEAH—Husband, no, not the stable! His wife may have the baby tonight. The stable's no place to birth a child.

JEREMY *(impatiently)*—Silence, wife! There is no choice. *(Men exit. Curtain falls.)*

Scene II

(The balcony above the main room in the inn. Have as many people as is practical, lying side by side in sleeping rolls on stage. Place MOTHER *and three girls in a group, center stage, with* ESTHER *on left,* MOTHER *on right.)*

MARDA—Esther, can you sleep?

ESTHER—No, the man down there snores too much. And I'm so excited! It is the first time I've slept at an inn. Last year when we came for the Passover, we slept in our tent.

RUTH—Shhhhh, you girls will wake up that child who cries. Then nobody will sleep.

MARDA—That man who came to the door just now. Did you see him?

ESTHER—Yes, wasn't that sad? His wife is expecting a baby!

RUTH—They went to the stable. What a place to spend the night!

MARDA—Oh, it'd be warm out there. The animals would make it warmer.

RUTH—And smelly! *(Giggles softly.)*

MOTHER—Hush, girls, quiet down. You're disturbing the others. *(Another person in a sleeping bag sits up, glares, then lies down again.)*

16

ESTHER—Yes, Mother.

(ESTHER *rolls, tosses, turns over, plumps her pillow, tries every way to get comfortable. Sits up, then slowly stands and walks to the window, stands looking out and starts counting stars.*)

ESTHER—One, two, three, four, five . . . (*Counts to 56 then goes back and lies down again. She can't sleep. Repeats her performance, starting where she left off—57, 58, 59, 60, 61, 62, 63. Leans out the window to see better. Turns around quickly and scrambles back to* MARDA *and* RUTH).

ESTHER—Marda, wake up. There's a star up there that's like no star I've ever seen.

MARDA (*Grumbles aloud and goes back to sleep.*)

(ESTHER *goes back to window again and looks out. Hurries back to* RUTH, *shakes her by the shoulder.*)

ESTHER—Ruth, come and see. It's a star like no other! I was counting stars and there's a bright one, *very* bright . . . and huge!

RUTH—Oh, Esther, keep still and go to sleep. Your imagination is busy again.

(ESTHER *goes back to the window. She listens.*)

ESTHER—There's music. Heavenly music is coming from somewhere. I hear it. I wonder what it means.

(ESTHER *goes back and shakes* MARDA).

ESTHER—Marda, quick. There's something happening. There's music! I can hear it!

MARDA—Esther, keep still! You're always dreaming up stuff.

ESTHER (*shakes* RUTH)—Ruth, come and listen. There's music. I hear it. I didn't dream it. It's happening.

(RUTH *doesn't stir.* ESTHER *goes back to window.*)

ESTHER—What does it mean? That bright star. It seems to be shining right on the stable. The music! I can hear it echoing across these Judean hills. What does it mean?

(ESTHER *pauses and watches, listening intently.*)

ESTHER—Oh, my, there are shepherds. I saw them just now. They're going to the stable. I thought I heard a baby cry. The woman who came too late for a bed must have had her baby.

(ESTHER *makes one more attempt to awaken the others, then gets braver and goes to her mother.*)

ESTHER—Mother, please come and see. Look at what's happening outside the window. I heard music, Mother. I heard a baby cry. There's a bright star.

MOTHER (*crossly*)—Esther, tomorrow I shall punish you for your disobedience. I said, GO TO SLEEP!

(*Another nearby guest stops snoring, sits up, glares, then lies down again, covers up his head.*)

17

ESTHER—But, Mother, it's different. The star is bright! There is music. Some shepherds came to the stable where the star is shining the brightest.
(Her mother isn't listening. ESTHER *goes back to the window.)*

ESTHER—Dear Lord, they won't wake up. They won't listen to me. I *know* this means something. And I believe YOU know what it is. I thank You, God, for letting me see. Help me now to understand.

(Curtain)

The Star of Bethlehem

(Position a star on the platform so it can be seen by everyone, and can be pointed toward by each speaker.)

READER—"I shall see him, but not now: I shall behold him, but not nigh: there shall come a Star out of Jacob, and a Sceptre shall rise out of Israel" (Numbers 24:17).

FIRST YOUTH—The Star of Jacob prophesied,
   A royal rod become a King.
  And Jesus' kingdom will abide,
   And finally conquer everything.

READER—"I will give him the morning star" (Revelation 2:28).

SECOND YOUTH—The morning star predicts the day,
   Appears before the light.
  So Jesus is the starlit Way,
   Whose light will overcome the night.

READER—"When they saw the star, they rejoiced with exceeding great joy" (Matthew 2:10).

THIRD YOUTH—And when the wise men saw the star,
   Rejoicing, they followed from afar.
  So then to Jesus gifts they bring,
   Acknowledging Him as Lord and King.

READER—The star was but a token of what our Lord would be.
  A symbol of His greatness, His love, and Deity.
  The prophets, wise men saw it as banner's truth unfurled;
  They knew it stood for Jesus, the Light of all the world.

—E. L. Russell

The Prodigal Dad

A Salvation Drama

by Evelyn Stenbock

Cast:

CHET AND BILL *(two businessmen)*
JESSIE (BILL'S *wife)*
BILLY, 13; PAM, 15; AMY, 7 (BILL'S *children)*
PARTICIPANTS IN SUNDAY SCHOOL PROGRAM

Scene I

(CHET and BILL sit in CHET'S office—CHET behind his desk, BILL in the visitor's chair. As the conversation progresses, they shift positions in natural ways according to their reactions.)

BILL: I really do appreciate your business, Chet—and more than that, it's a pleasure to deal with you. *(Pause)* Seems that there's something about you that I don't detect in many people.

CHET: It's a pleasure to do business with you, too, Bill. And as for being different, well—I guess I am different.

BILL: You really are.

CHET: I'm—well, I'm a Christian.

BILL: You mean the "born again" kind?

CHET: Right.

BILL: That's what I like about you. You're so open. Not many people admit to being born again. I mean, it sounds pretty fanatical.

CHET: I guess I am a fanatic.

BILL: Come off it! You're not fanatical. You've never crammed religion down my throat!

CHET: Frankly, I'm always hesitant about bringing up the subject until I feel sure a person is ready to listen. Cramming my beliefs down your throat wouldn't help either one of us us very much if you were unwilling to listen.

19

BILL: I guess that's true. *(Pause)* So what do you believe?

CHET: First of all, I believe that God can change a man's life to such an extent that he becomes a totally new person. (BILL *leans forward to concentrate on what is being said.)* The reason I believe this is because God changed me three years ago.

BILL: Changed you? From what to what?

CHET: From a boozing businessman—cheating, money-mad, scheming— (BILL *interrupts.)*

BILL: Now wait a minute. You've never been like that.

CHET: I was. But God changed me. (BILL *studies Chet's face for some time.* CHET *looks steadily into his eyes but doesn't speak.)*

BILL: You wouldn't lie to me.

CHET: Not now I wouldn't.

BILL: You really were that bad.

CHET: My colleagues here at the office—my wife—my kids will tell you I was. Linda, my wife, got saved first. She prayed for me and, well, I couldn't help but see how different she was; so before long I began to listen to what she had to say about the Bible, about sin, and about salvation. One Sunday I— (BILL *interrupts.)*

BILL: You know, I've really been struggling with that.

CHET: With what?

BILL: With sin and . . . what you call salvation. It's something I really don't understand. I mean, we all sin—at least I know I do.

CHET: You're right on target, Bill. The Bible says we're all sinners. "For all have sinned, and come short of the glory of God."

BILL: So. We're all human beings. I mean, we can't be perfect.

CHET: That's true enough. Our sinful nature keeps dragging us down, and no matter how hard we try, we can't seem to pick ourselves up by the boot-straps and become more holy.

BILL: How well I know that!

CHET: You sound as if you've tried.

BILL: Tried! *(Stands and paces the floor.)* You don't know how hard I've tried! *(Looks at Chet.)* I suppose I might as well lay all of it out on the table. I'm torn up inside. I'm not going home for Christmas. I was divorced three months ago.

CHET: *(stands up):* Bill, I'm sorry. I had no idea. *(He comes around the desk.)*

BILL: I try to put it out of my mind when I'm working. Back at the motel evenings, I agonize over it, rehearsing the whole thing over in my mind until I nearly go mad. Why did it all happen? *(Paces the floor before continuing.)* Jessie is such a live wire! I mean we had a ball from the day we met until— *(Sits down, dejected.* CHET *sits on the desk, fiddling with a pen.)*

CHET: Until something went sour.

BILL: Yeah. My traveling didn't help, mind you. Jessie was lonesome—so was I, but how was she to know that? In her mind I was living high: fancy motels, expense accounts, meals, entertainment. Her fantasies were a far cry from reality. Here I was, flying from motel to motel, eating tasteless food, drinking more than I wanted just to keep customers happy, and spending most evenings staring at a TV screen that I never really saw.

CHET: You got children?

BILL: Three of them. Bill's 13, Pam is 15, and Amy's—let's see: she's seven, I guess. Their mother has custody of them, of course. I'll have to set up housekeeping this summer so they can stay with me for a while. *(Pause, with a short laugh)* I'm looking forward to that—the kids, I mean, not the housekeeping.

CHET: Does Jessie take them to church?

BILL: Church? Listen—religion is the farthest thing from that gal's mind. No way!

CHET: You mean you never went to church as a family?

BILL: Never.

CHET: When you were a kid, you went to Sunday School, I suppose.

BILL: No, to tell you the truth, I never did.

CHET: Your kids didn't go to Sunday School, either?

BILL: No. They asked a time or two if they could go with friends, but we didn't think it was a good idea. I'm a little sorry now. I suppose those kids were from pretty good families.

CHET: Tell me, Bill, has anyone ever explained the gospel to you?

BILL: The what?

CHET: The gospel. The way of salvation through Christ. The gospel is the good news that God is willing to forgive our sins on the merit of Jesus' death on the Cross. *(Pause)* Look, when I spoke to you about the possibility of one's life being changed by God, I had no idea yours was in such a mixed-up state.

BILL: Mess is a better word. *(Sighs.)* I could use a change. Tell me more.

CHET *(goes back to his chair):* We've already established that all human beings are sinners, right?

BILL: I know I am.

CHET: And according to the Bible, "The wages of sin is death." Sin has separated us from God—that's eternal death. In order to reconcile us to God—to make peace between God and us—Christ died for our sins. You know the Easter story, don't you?

21

BILL: You mean the Crucifixion?

CHET: Yes.

BILL: It was a terrible way for a good man to die.

CHET: Jesus Christ was far more than a good man. He was, and is, the Son of the Most High God. (BILL *listens intently.*) God's plan to save us from our sin included sending His Son, Jesus, from heaven to earth. You see, Jesus didn't come into being there in Bethlehem. He always was, with God. They must have talked it over, and He willingly agreed to humble himself and come to earth, for our sakes. His coming is what Christmas is all about. There's a Bible verse most children learn that goes like this: "For God so loved the world, that he gave his only begotten Son, that whosoever believeth in him should not perish, but have everlasting life."

BILL: The baby born in a cattle barn. The shepherds and wise men—

CHET: The angels that announced that Baby's birth, and the star which miraculously guided the wise men to the Child. You see, Bill, Jesus was no ordinary Baby. He was God dressed in human flesh. The Christmas Baby was born to be the Savior of the world, and when He died on the Cross, it was not defeat. Shedding His blood was part of God's plan. The Bible says, "Without shedding of blood is no remission" for sins.

BILL: You believe that?

CHET: Yes, I do.

BILL: I wish I could.

CHET: You can. God himself will help you to believe. You've heard of "God the Father, God the Son, and God the Holy Spirit."

BILL: Vaguely.

CHET: The Holy Spirit works quietly in our lives, helping us to understand and believe. God is waiting like a Father with outstretched arms, hoping you'll come to Him. They make it as easy as possible—all you have to do is say okay. You pray and acknowledge your sin to God, and when you do that, you'll discover that you really do believe—you'll find the faith to ask Jesus to come in to cleanse your heart and take over your life. *(Pause.)* Would you like to do that now, Bill?

BILL: Right here?

CHET: Yes.

BILL *(lengthy, restless pause):* Not yet, Chet. Thanks a million for explaining it to me. It may be the answer to my despair. Truthfully, I'm so lonely and discouraged I'm ready to try anything. *(Gets up to leave.)* I'd better get going. I've got another call to make before I call it quits for the day.

CHET: Are you busy tonight?

BILL: Busy? *(Laughs cynically.)* Sure. I'm real busy.

CHET (hesitates some): This may sound crazy, but my kids are in a Christmas program at our church. Why don't you come with us? After the program we'll go to the house and discuss this some more.

BILL: Are you serious?

CHET: Of course. I'll pick you up at 6:30. (Both exit.)

Scene II

(BILL, CHET, and CHET'S WIFE enter as the Sunday School program begins, and take a seat near the front. Insert here the departmental songs and exercises you have planned, closing this portion of the Sunday School program with announcements and offering, and a brief explanation of the gospel by the pastor.)

Scene III

(BILL'S home: a living room scene with tree and presents. JESSIE and the three children are in casual dress and sitting around the room. JESSIE is crying.)

BILLY: Aw, Mom! Cut out the crying!

PAM (going to JESSIE to comfort her, and starting to choke up herself): Mom, why did Daddy leave us? Doesn't he love us at all? Christmas without him is awful.

JESSIE (raises head and dries tears): I'm sorry, kids. (Sniffs.) It's Christmas and I know we have to make the best of it without Dad. But (pause) I miss him so much, and I wish he could be with us for Christmas.

AMY: Do you think he'll bring me a present?

JESSIE: Amy, dear (reaches out and hugs her), we don't even know if your dad is thinking of us, let alone buying presents.

BILLY: But I know he is! Dad loves Christmas!

JESSIE: But we don't know he's coming. Don't get your hopes up. You'll be lucky if he remembers to call you for Christmas.

BILLY: I'll call him!

JESSIE: You don't know where he is, son.

BILLY: Grandma will know. I'll call and ask her. Maybe he's going there for Christmas.

JESSIE: You said he told you last week he wasn't going to Grandma's.

AMY: We bought him presents.

PAM: All my hard-earned baby-sitting money. He's got to come home.

JESSIE: Pam (firm), how often do I have to tell you this is not your father's home.

23

AMY: We prayed and asked God to bring him home for Christmas. Peggy's mother said God answers prayers even when little girls pray them.

BILLY *(shouts angrily, stands up, and turn away from the rest):* Maybe God didn't hear your prayers. How do you know there's a God? *(Tone changes to self-pity.)* If there was a God, He wouldn't leave a guy without a dad. *(Turns his back to the others.)*

JESSIE: Billy! *(Changes to soft voice.)* Oh, Billy, my past life has done you no good! *(Stands up and goes to him.)* I'm sorry, Billy. How I regret my past . . . ungodly living. I know if I had been a Christian six months ago, your dad would never have left home.

PAM: You've really changed, Mom. (MOTHER *turns around.*)

AMY: You have, Mom. You're just like Peggy's mother.

JESSIE *(sitting down, and holding* AMY, *who sits beside her, close):* What a nice compliment, Amy. *(Pause)* Well, I've got a long way to go to be like Peggy's mom—and she says, anyway, that I should try to be like Jesus, not like her.

AMY: She's like Jesus.

JESSIE: Really, she is, honey. I'm so glad you brought her over that day; if it hadn't been for my worries about who would take care of you, with your father gone, I'd have killed myself. (BILLY *turns back and joins the rest again.)*

PAM: I'm so glad Amy had the sense to run and tell Peggy's mother you were screaming.

AMY: I was scared to death!

JESSIE: Oh, Pam . . . I'm so ashamed.

AMY: But she came right over and saved you.

JESSIE: No, Amy. She didn't save me. She told me about Jesus and how He could save me. He did save me, and it changed my whole life. I feel like a different woman!

PAM: You are a different woman! That's why I accepted the Lord. I knew He must be real, to do such a big change in you.

BILLY *(wistfully):* I wish I could have gone to spend Christmas with Dad.

JESSIE: Son, you know I would have let you go—

BILLY: My dad doesn't want me with him.

JESSIE: I'm sure that's not true, Billy. Don't get to blaming your dad for everything. The divorce was my fault. I was the one who . . . *(sighs.)* Oh—I don't know. There's no sense in whipping myself over the past. I wish he'd accept the Lord.

PAM: Forget that! He'd be impossible to change! Wow! Remember that temper? And his hangovers. *(Mimics father.)* "Pam, for the last time—turn down that stereo! My head is splitting."

JESSIE: Remember my temper and my hangovers. If God could change me, He could change your father, too.

AMY: I'm still going to pray for him to be saved. Peggy's mother—

BILLY *(interrupts with loud voice):* That will never happen!

AMY *(shouts):* It will too!

BILLY: It will not! Dad hates religious people.

AMY: How do you know? *(As she is speaking, the doorbell rings.* JESSIE *goes toward the door, speaking.)*

JESSIE: Hush, you kids! What a thing to fight about! *(Opens door.)* Bill! (BILL *steps in and hesitates. The children stand up and for a brief moment freeze with surprised looks on their faces; then they rush toward him.)*

BILL: I should have called to ask permission to visit the children, Jessie. I just couldn't stay away at Christmas. And I— *(He embraces the children as he talks.)*

JESSIE: Bill, I—I wanted so badly to apologize for the past. *(The group moves back to center stage.)* I've changed, really I have. Come sit down. We've been praying you'd come.

BILL *(moves toward her expectantly):* You have? You've been praying?

JESSIE: I've changed, Bill. I turned my whole life—

AMY: Mom got saved!

BILL: Jessie!

JESSIE: I did, Bill. Please, listen to reason. I know we've always scoffed at religious people, and I don't want to fight at Christmastime!

BILL: Fight! *(The children look on fearfully.)*

JESSIE: You never wanted the kids to go to church. You were wrong, Bill . . . You've hated religious people . . . Now I am one!

BILL: So am I, Sweetheart! I went to a Sunday School program last night and accepted Christ!

JESSIE: Bill! *(They embrace.)*

A Reading

A slightly smudged, lopsided Christmas tree star
Was carefully carried home—'twas not very far—

Clutched in the hands of a five-year-old boy,
When all of a sudden out jumped Bill and Roy.

"Well, what's this crummy thing that you made today!"
But, pulling back, little Eddie ran away.

The big bullies laughed as they chased after him
Down Palmer Lane towards John, Craig, and Kim.

"Hey, what's the hurry?" they called as he rushed past
And ran up the steps, safely home at last.

Hoping they hadn't seen the tears in his eyes,
He sneaked in the bedroom with his surprise.

Later, after supper, he shyly held it out.
"Oh, my!" exclaimed his parents. "Without any doubt,

Your special ornament is the best by far!"
So a slightly smudged, lopsided Christmas tree star

Proudly sits on top of their evergreen tree,
Reminding everyone who comes in to see

Of Bethlehem's star and God's gift of Joy.
Yes, love makes the difference to the parents of a boy!

Even a small child has an important part;
True value is something felt in your heart.

—Elaine Hardt

Thoughts of Christmas

Thoughts of Christmas come to
    mind,
As I send cards of greetings,
With each verse and line.

Thoughts of Christmas from long
    ago
Are felt in my heart as I watch the
    skies,
And hope for winter snow.

Thoughts of Christmas goodwill and
    cheer
Seem even more meaningful,
When loved ones are near.

Thoughts of Christmas and deco-
    rated trees
Make me feel joy when others I can
    please.

Thoughts of Christmas and Jesus'
    birth as a King
Give me hope and love,
As I hear Christmas bells ring.

Thoughts of Christmas and all that
    God has given;
Shows me the truth and the way—
Our King has surely risen!

—Wanda E. Brunstetter

When the Light Came

by Cora M. Owen

(A reading for a teen costumed as a shepherd. Should be dramatized by a group of children as reading is presented.)

Scene—Shepherds seated around open fire. Reader stands to one side of scene.

READER—I have a wonderful story to tell. It happened a long time ago.

It was cold in the fields that night. The stars glittered in a faraway sky. We shepherds huddled close to the fire. Its warmth made me drowsy as I listened to the low tones of my fellow shepherds talking of the happenings of the day. The sheep flocked together a short distance away with an occasional bleat breaking the silence of the night. We had to keep a close watch on them, or some would wander away and be lost. *(Bright light shines on group.)*

Suddenly—a light! (SHEPHERDS *are startled.*) So brightly it illuminated the area around us! It nearly blinded our eyes. We covered our faces and fell to the ground, filled with wonder and fear. (SHEPHERDS *fall on faces to the ground.)* What was happening?

My heart was beating so fast that it felt as though it would jump from my body. I trembled and shook as I peeped through my fingers at the light-filled sky. What a sight!

(SHEPHERDS *look up as an* ANGEL *appears.)*

I heard a voice speaking to us. I saw—it must be an angel! It was an angel! I had heard how angels appeared to our people in the past, bringing messages from God. Now an angel was speaking to us. We were chosen to hear God's message!

He said, "Don't be afraid. I bring you good news which will bring joy to all people. Unto you is born this day in Bethlehem a Savior, who is Christ the Lord. You will find the Baby lying in a manger."

(Other ANGELS *appear.)*

Then as I watched, many more angels appeared. They were glorifying and praising God. They sang, "Glory to God in the highest, and on earth peace, good will toward men."

(ANGELS *depart.)*

They went away as quickly as they had come. We rose from the ground, rubbing our eyes, hardly believing what we had seen and heard.

(SHEPHERDS *rise.)*

I said, "It was a message from God. The Messiah has come! Let us go to Bethlehem to find Him!" I was so happy I could hardly speak. The Messiah—

our people had waited so long. He had come at last! I wanted to be the first one to see Him.

(SHEPHERDS *start to Bethlehem.*)

Leaving one man to watch the sheep, we started for the city. I hurried ahead of the others, stumbling over rocks and sticks in my path. Half walking, half running, I came into the streets of Bethlehem. The angel had said a manger. That meant a stable. The largest stable in town belonged to the inn. Something guided me there. I heard cattle lowing softly and the thump of their hoofs as they moved restlessly.

(MARY *and* JOSEPH *at manger.* SHEPHERDS *enter.*)

I hurriedly entered. There before me I saw the sweetest, most precious Baby I had ever seen. I loved Him instantly. We fell on our knees before that manger to worship Him.

I knew this was Messiah. I believed in my heart. This was Jesus, my Savior and King!

(SHEPHERDS *leave.*)

We ran outside, anxious to tell everyone what had come to pass. We shouted our message—"Messiah has come! We have been told by God. We have seen Him! He is here!" People wondered at our words. Some thought us mad, but we knew the truth.

We returned to our flocks, saying, "Praise God! Our Savior has come! Glory to God! Glory to God!" His joy filled our hearts on this night of nights when the Light came.

It's Christmastime

It must be time for Christmas;
  I feel it in the air.
A radiant star is in the sky,
  And music's everywhere.

No wise man's gift have I to give;
  Christ doesn't want a thing,
Except this broken heart of mine,
  Which now I gladly bring.

Just the thought of Christmastime
  Can make the teardrops start.
All year round, I wish it were
  Christmas in my heart.

It must be Christmastime again;
  I feel it in the air.
There's peace on earth, goodwill
    toward men,
  And God's love's everywhere.

—*Gean D. Smith*

The Manger

As the wise men searched the
    heavens,
  Looking for a star,
I, too, searched and am no more
  A stranger from afar.

As shepherds, led by angels' song,
  Were guided that dark night
Unto the manger, I, too, come
  From darkness unto light.

As long ago when I heard His voice,
  I come again today
Unto the little manger where
  The Baby Jesus lay.

I come, I see, and I embrace
  This Infant so sublime,
And praise the Lord for His sweet
    Gift
  This blessed Christmastime.

—*Gean D. Smith*

28

Christmas Interview

By Evelyn Minshull

(Television news reporter stands with hand mike. He watches unseen people walk by. While he stands, Luke 2:1-3 is read.)

FLAVIUS *(after scripture reading):* Good evening, ladies and gentlemen. This is Antonius Flavius, your roving reporter, bringing you on-the-spot coverage on the event which has the empire on the move—the census-taking and taxation ordered by Caesar Augustus, our revered emperor. I'm standing this evening on a busy street in the outskirts of Bethlehem. Bethlehem, normally, is not an active town—the most exciting event of a day likely to be a stubborn donkey stalling traffic. But with Israelites of every size, age, and description returning to the quote "City of David" unquote to register, there's more than enough action now! Here's a travel-worn gentleman, coming this way. Oh, sir! Sir! (JEHORAM *enters.*)

JEHORAM: Were you calling me?

FLAVIUS: Yes, could I ask you a few questions, sir?

JEHORAM: If it won't take long. And if you're not going to ask where you can find lodging! I've been to three inns already, and the answer is always the same.

FLAVIUS: Then I promise I won't ask you that. For the sake of our listeners, I wonder if you would tell me why you have come here to register. Why not to Jerusalem? Or some other city?

JEHORAM: But I am of the tribe of Judah, a descendant of David!

FLAVIUS: I see. And this is—the city of David.

JEHORAM: Quite right. A beautiful city, isn't it? But more important than its beauty is its promise.

FLAVIUS: Promise? I don't believe I understand.

JEHORAM: The promise of the prophets! They have said that from this city—

29

from my family!—from the root of Jesse, shall come the Promised One, the Messiah! How exciting this has been! All of my life, when times have been hard to bear, the promise has glowed against the darkness of trouble and despair—

FLAVIUS: Ah, yes. Well, I must be getting on to another interview. Thank you, sir, and I hope you find a room. Good-bye. (JEHORAM *hurries off.)* As the gentleman said, the housing problem is acute here tonight. There's an inn just up the street a bit. Perhaps we could move there and talk to someone in control. (JACOB *enters, sweeping sidewalk.)* Ah, there he is himself, a prospering innkeeper, Jacob, son of Levi. Well, Jacob, how is business?

JACOB: Terrible, terrible, terrible.

FLAVIUS: Terrible? But how busy would you want to be? Are you often this busy?

JACOB: Never before, and I should hope never again. All day long it has been rush, rush, rush—"Get me this," "Get me that," "Do this," "Do that," "Don't you have a larger room than this?" "Look at that view!" "What terrible service!" *(Pause)* I shall go out of my mind if this goes on much longer. Already my wife is lying down with a sick headache, and I'm sorry I did not think of a sick headache first, though goodness knows where I could find a cot to stretch out on! It is not pleasure, I can tell you, to turn people away from the door.

FLAVIUS: And to lose all those silver pieces for a night's lodging!

JACOB *(thoughtfully):* But no, more than that is the pain of seeing their tired faces, their looks of despair. Just a short time ago, there came a couple who touched me deeply. She was expecting a child, poor thing, and so very tired. And he—so concerned, so gentle.

FLAVIUS: How far had they come?

JACOB: From Nazareth.

FLAVIUS: All the way from Nazareth?

JACOB: He leading the donkey on which she rode. I told them, of course, that there was no room. The looks on their faces—I couldn't bear it. As they turned to leave, I told them about the stable.

FLAVIUS: What about the stable?

JACOB: That they could stay there, if they wished. It isn't much, I know. But a place to keep off the chill. And the hay is fresh and sweet. They were glad of the shelter it offered. There was something about them—I had the strongest feeling that the best I would have to offer on a slow day would not be fine enough. And yet—when they settled into the stable, they made it seem quite fine enough. It was strange. I have not told my wife of it as yet. The sick headache, you know . . . and she is so tired. *(Jacob exits.)*

FLAVIUS *(yawning):* I'm tired, too. Almost as tired as though I had walked from Nazareth, leading a donkey. But fortunately I have a room in which to rest the night. In this very inn, as a matter of fact. Well, ladies and gentlemen, unless something unexpected happens tonight, this will be all you'll be hearing from me until tomorrow. Antonius Flavius, over and out. And thanks for listening!

CHOIR: *"It Came upon a Midnight Clear"*

FLAVIUS: Ladies and gentlemen, the most astounding events have been rumored to take place this night! Whether they are true or not—and it seems most unlikely that they are—they should make entertaining listening. An hour or so ago, some shabby shepherds scrambled into town, half incoherent with a combination of excitement and disbelief. They were babbling about (SHEPHERD *with staff enters),* but here comes one now. I'll let him tell you his own story. Shepherd! Over here! What is your name?

SHEPHERD: My name? That isn't important! It is HIS name that matters. Christ, he is to be called. The Son of the Highest. The Son of Man. The Son of God! The Messiah!

FLAVIUS: The Messiah? Someone before mentioned Him.

SHEPHERD: My people have always spoken of Him, of His coming—but always it was as a fantasy—no, not a fantasy, something that would *one* day come true, but not for us to see. And now it has happened!

FLAVIUS: Our listening audience would be interested in *why* you are so sure this great event has happened. Would you tell them what I heard you telling the innkeeper and the others gathered outside the stable?

SHEPHERD: Gladly! I'd like to tell the whole world, and I will, if I have the chance! *(Pause for breath)* We were out on the hills, watching the sheep. It was a night like any other. Simon was grumbling about the cold, and Amos, who wanted to get some sleep, was grumbling about the grumbling. Joash had taken a turn about the hill to make sure everything was all right, and it was. Just like any other night. More peaceful than many. And then it happened!

FLAVIUS: Yes, go on.

SHEPHERD: The most marvelous thing! Joash noticed it first. A glow in the sky, growing swiftly, and then the angel!

FLAVIUS: You were certain right away that it was an angel?

SHEPHERD: We were too frightened, I think, to understand what it was. Just this white glowing being, speaking in glorious tones, saying those marvelous things—

FLAVIUS: *What* marvelous things?

SHEPHERD: Let me see if I can remember the exact words—*(optional scripture—Luke 2:10b-12)*

FLAVIUS: And then you came here, to Bethlehem.

SHEPHERD: Yes, just as we had been told. And everything was as the angel had said. Praise Jehovah! Now if you'll excuse me, I must go and tell others.

FLAVIUS: And there you have it, folks—direct from Bethlehem—news of such a nature that—if it is true—might well change the shape of the future. And if it is rumor—what harm has been done? At least the boredom, the tiresomeness, of this census taking has been lightened. One can't help wondering how our exalted emperor will react to the news, should he hear it. This might well be worth following up, when I get back to Jerusalem.

(Pause)

Perhaps you are wondering if I visited the stable myself and saw the child. I did. The parents were none other than the young couple who arrived earlier this evening. The child was . . . much like any child. It was strange, seeing him there in the manger. Sad, really, that a newborn should be housed with animals. But it was not an unpleasant scene. The mother glowed with love. The father was as proud as we expect new fathers to be. And the child—somehow I keep coming back to him. The glow of starlight radiated from the hay, making a light about his head. At least I assumed it was starlight. What else could it have been? But no more for tonight. This is Antonius Flavius, signing off again. Unless something else of a startling nature occurs, you may not be hearing from me again until I speak to you from Jerusalem. Antonius Flavius, over and out.

CHOIR: *"O Holy Night!"*

FLAVIUS: Good evening, ladies and gentlemen! Antonius Flavius here, bringing you the first post-census interview show. There was a time, in Bethlehem, when I thought we might be having a highly unusual show in Jerusalem. But nothing has come of the night which seemed to offer so much hope to those excitable shepherds who thought they'd seen a vision, and so rushed to do homage to a quite ordinary child, in a stable nursery. But enough of that. In a moment, a most distinguished visitor will grace our program— His Excellency, King Herod! He will be explaining the reasons for the emperor's census, and the success he feels the venture will have, when all results are in. He should be here momentarily.

(Pause)

Ah, here he comes now! Your Excellency, might we have a word with you?

HEROD: Yes, yes, what is it? Ah, you're the young man who's interviewing me?

FLAVIUS: Yes, Your Excellency. I fully realize how busy you are, but our listeners are anxious to hear what you have to say.

HEROD: Of course. Though common people have little understanding of the burdens and thoughts of a king.

(Pause)

Hmmm. Very strange. (WISE MAN *enters.*) Who is he, I wonder?

FLAVIUS *(turning to look):* Ladies and gentlemen, you would never believe the magnificent sight we are beholding! A richly dressed man—looking a king himself—is striding toward us! In the distance are two more such men, and camels, as richly harnessed as their riders are dressed! What a sight! Merchants, scurrying about their tasks, have stopped to gape!

HEROD: I thought you were going to interview me!

FLAVIUS: Enough time for that later. *(Calling to* WISE MAN MELCHIOR*)* Sir! Sir! Would you speak to us, please? What is your name? Where are you from?

MELCHIOR: My companions and I come from the Far East on a most important pilgrimage. We have traveled long and hazardous miles, but the quest has been worth the danger, and now we near the end of the journey!

HEROD: And what is your quest? You have not come to make war on us—have you?

MELCHIOR *(laughing):* Quite the opposite! We have come to worship!

HEROD: To worship . . . the Hebrew God?

MELCHIOR: To worship a king.

HEROD: I am king here!

MELCHIOR: You? But—but this was to be an infant king! It has been promised in ancient writings. We have seen His star in the East and have hurried as fast as we can—

HEROD: An infant king? A—a baby?

MELCHIOR: So we have been told. We have brought Him gold and frankincense and myrrh. And we long to kneel in worship before Him. Perhaps you could give us news of Him!

FLAVIUS *(to* MELCHIOR): What will you and your friends do now?

MELCHIOR: We will continue . . . as long as it takes to find Him. *(Begins to walk off.)*

HEROD: Wait! Wait! (MELCHIOR *turns.)* I—I want you to promise me something. If—if you *do* find Him . . . will you come back and tell me where? I—I want to worship him also.

(WISE MAN exits.)
(Pause)

FLAVIUS: Well! What excitement, ladies and gentlemen! Your Excellency, have you ever seen anything like this before?

HEROD *(inattentively):* No. Never.

FLAVIUS: Our ordinary interview business will seem tame after this.

HEROD: You'll . . . have to excuse me. I . . . don't feel like talking now. *(Exits.)*

FLAVIUS: Well, ladies and gentlemen, what an exciting turn of events this has been! Did you notice the mention of the star? There was an exceedingly bright star over Bethlehem the night the shepherds hurried into town with their tale of angels. And the promise of a king! That was mentioned that night, too. And a newborn child. Could this be the child of the stable? I wonder. I wonder . . . This is Antonius Flavius, signing off for tonight with one additional thought. I have a feeling . . . a very strong one—that the Roman Empire—and perhaps the world—hasn't heard the last of that unusual child. Over and out, and thanks for listening.

CHOIR: *"Star of the East"*

'Tis Not the Day

'Tis not the day, as much the deed
   That makes the birth of Christ so
     real.
'Tis what He brings, fulfilling need,
   Producing joy and hope we feel.
So we rejoice to keep this day
   To honor Christ for glorious birth
And we unite to sing and pray,
   And may His kingdom fill the
     earth.
We gladly come and homage bring
   To Him who offers sin's release!
In Bethlehem He's born a King—
   And now He reigns, the Prince of
     Peace!

—E. L. Russell

The Mystery Box

(Three teens enter, one at a time, look at a large Christmas box, recite their piece, and move on out. The fourth picks up the card, reads it, and shouts, "It's for me!")

1ST TEEN—

I wonder what this box contains?
   What gift is locked inside?
Is it a toy, or clothes to wear?
   What does this package hide?

2ND TEEN—

I wonder who this gift is for?
   Who is the lucky one?
Is it for Mother, or for Dad?
   For daughter, or for son?

3RD TEEN—

Who sent or left this mystery gift?
   Who wrapped it with such care?
Whoever it is that he may be,
   I'm glad he wants to share!

4TH TEEN—"It's for me!"

'Tis God who gave this greatest gift—
   The gift from heaven above!
And it's a gift for everyone—
   The gift of God's own love!

—E. L. Russell

Ode to the Unwritten Pages

Midnight strikes and the old year's
   gone.
We close the tablets we've written
   on.

Pages soiled with blunder and regret.
Stories written with eyelids wet!

Within our reach, before us laid,
Twelve new volumes the Lord has
   made.

With unmarred pages, pure and
   white,
For us our daily lives to write.

With hope and doubt, with joy and
   fear,
We write the story of another year!

—Paul Taylor

"For to You Is Born . . ."

O Holy Child, sleeping softly,
   Beneath the shining star,
Did You know the angels sang?
   Shepherds watched from afar?

Holy Infant, sweetly stirring,
   As Your mother and Joseph gaze,
Did You know You were the One
   The world would ever praise?

Sovereign Babe, so small and pure,
   Did You know that countless hearts
Were waiting for the light and truth
   Your presence still imparts?

And did You know that You would be
   Rejected and crucified,
By a world of men so sinful,
   Who would deny You died?

O Lamb of God, give us the grace
   To rejoice in Your Father's plan:
Your holy birth and sacrifice—
   The only cure for man!

—Ruth M. Walsh

Good News

V. P.

Verla Peterson

Good news—something's happened in Beth-le-hem; Good news—did you hear the an-gels sing? Good news—don't you fear, there is great joy here! Hal-le-lu-jah with us sing. Good news—He's the King of all kings!

Worship and Praise

V. P.

(Round)

Verla Peterson

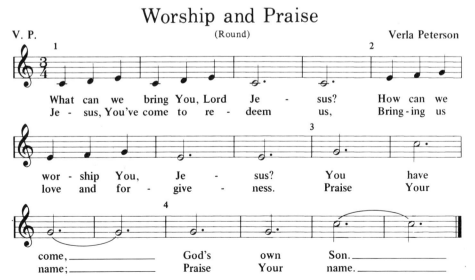

What can we bring You, Lord Je - sus? How can we
Je - sus, You've come to re - deem us, Bring-ing us

wor - ship You, Je - sus? You have
love and for - give - ness. Praise Your

come, _____ God's own Son. _____
name; _____ Praise Your name. _____

35

The Gift of God's Son

A. S.

Annette Seaton

1. In a hum-ble man-ger, _____ in a low-ly cat-tle stall, _____ Came to us a stran-ger _____ who was giv-en for us all. _____ The Son of God the Fa-ther _____ and per-fect Son of man, _____

2. Now there's hope for liv-ing _____ in this Ba-by born to-day. _____ Through the Fa-ther's giv-ing _____ He's pro-vid-ed us a way. _____ God gave His Son a ran-som, _____ an of-fer-ing for sin, _____

His name is Christ the Sav - ior,\
That we might have sal - va - tion,

the ful - fill - ment of God's plan.\
ev - er - last - ing life in Him.

Chorus

And\
So we sing

glo - ry, glo-ry in the high-est to God; Glo - ry, our Re-deem-er has

come.___ Yes, we sing glo-ry, glo-ry in the high - est to God___

rit.

For the pre-cious gift of God's Son.

Alleluia

J. P.

Joe Pinson

Al - le, al - le - lu, al - le - lu - ia. Al - le, al - le - lu, al - le - lu - ia.

1. Mar - y had a ba - by, a ver - y spe - cial child.
2. An - gels sang a - bout Him a ver - y spe - cial song.
3. Wise men saw it shin - ing, a ver - y spe - cial star.

Mar - y had a ba - by, a ver - y spe - cial child.
An - gels sang a - bout Him a ver - y spe - cial song.
Wise men saw it shin - ing, a ver - y spe - cial star.

My Heart Sings

J. P.

Joe Pinson

Refrain

My heart sings to the King of Kings, Je - sus the on - ly Son.

My heart sings to the King of Kings, praise to the Ho - ly One.

1. Mar - y knew the words were true the an - gel spoke when he came:
2. Jo - seph went where he was sent with Mar - y great with her child.
3. An - gels sang and heav - ens rang to tell the tid - ings of joy:

"You have been cho-sen to bear a son, and the Lord will_ bless your name."
Je - sus was born in a sta - ble bare to the Vir - gin_ pure and mild.
"Go to the cit - y of Beth - le - hem and give thanks for the ba - by boy."